Nena
the
Whale

Rick C. Miller

Trilogy Christian Publishers
A Wholly Owned Subsidary of Trinity Broadcasting Network
2442 Michelle Drive
Tustin, CA 92780

Cover design by: Cornerstone Creative Solutions

For information, address Trilogy Christian Publishing
Rights Department, 2442 Michelle Drive, Tustin, Ca 92780.
Trilogy Christian Publishing/ TBN and colophon are trademarks of Trinity Broadcasting Network.

For information about special discounts for bulk purchases, please contact Trilogy Christian Publishing.

Manufactured in the United States of America

10 9 8 7 6 5 4 3 2 1

Library of Congress Cataloging-in-Publication Data is available.

ISBN 978-1-63769-104-5 (Print Book)
ISBN 978-1-63769-105-2 (ebook)

Dedicated to all the children
I taught in Sunday School

Nena the whale
Is a tale to tell
I will share you this story
I know it so well

3

Now Nena was swimming
At the old swimming hole
She saw her friend Barry
He was feeling kinda low

Barry was a lonely fish
He was always so sad
Nena wanted so badly
To make him feel glad

Barry was grumpy
His face was so long
But Nena had something
A nice happy song

7

Do a happy dance
Do a happy glance
Let your happiness
Shine through

Do a happy giggle
Do a happy wiggle
Let your happiness
Be you

Barry looked at Nena
And started to laugh
"I don't like your singing
You sound like a giraffe

I don't like to dance
I don't like to giggle
I don't like to glance
And I will never wiggle

So leave me alone
And let me be sad
I don't want to be happy
You're making me mad"

Nena was persistent
She never gives in
"I'll be back to see you, Barry
Because you're my good friend"

Barry blew a bubble
And said, "Friends are not true
They laugh and they tease me
And make me feel blue"

Nena was sad
And thought for a while
I know a friend
That will give you a smile

A friend with a love
So real and so true
A friend who will always
Always know you

Barry was silent
Than blew another bubble
"This friend that you speak of
Causes me trouble"

You say that your friend
Has a love that's so real
Why would he like me
I'm not a big deal"

Nena said, "Listen
You have a lot to gain
He knows who you are
You're not a whatshisname

My friend made the mountains
And expanded the sky
Created a flower
And taught the birds how to fly

Brought light in the darkness
Put water in the ocean
Created the world
And put it in motion

His name is Jesus
A good friend to me
He's faithful and honest
And good company

So take a swim
And hold on fast
He'll give you new life
That will last and last

He will tell you his story
How he died on the cross
Rose from the dead
And redeemed who was lost

So just ask Jesus
To be your friend
He's not like a fable
No need to pretend"

The grumpy was gone
With a smile on his face
Barry had a happy
You could never erase!

Barry found Jesus
A friend so true
Do you know Jesus?
He's waiting for you!

For God so loved the world (you)
That he gave his only son (Jesus)
That whoever believes in him
Shall not perish, but have everlasting life

Salvation Prayer

If you want to ask Jesus
into your heart
Begin with this prayer
That's a good place
To start

Jesus will listen
to the words that you pray
Say that your sorry
For the times
When you stray

Ask Jesus to come
And give you new light
Enter your life
And Turn wrong into right

Trust Jesus to be
Your savior and Friend
He will live in your heart
There will be no end,

Ricky John

CPSIA information can be obtained
at www.ICGtesting.com
Printed in the USA
LVHW070753300721
694127LV00009B/213